An interview with

Michelle Magorian

EGMONT

Other authors in
the series:

Enid Blyton, Theresa Breslin,
Gillian Cross, Anne Fine, Jamila Gavin,
Michael Morpurgo, Jenny Nimmo,
Jacqueline Wilson, J.K. Rowling

Kate Agnew works part-time at the Children's Bookshop,
Muswell Hill, and as a children's book consultant.
She is co-author of *Children At War*, a book about children's
fiction set in war-time, and has been a Smarties and
Whitbread judge.

First published in Great Britain 1999 by Mammoth.
This edition published 2003 by Egmont Books Limited,
239 Kensington High Street, London W8 6SA.

Interview questions, design and typesetting © 1999 Egmont Books Limited
Interview answers © 1999 Michelle Magorian
Michelle's Books © 1999 Kate Agnew
The Front Room © 1983 Michelle Magorian
Illustrations for 'The Front Room' © 1983 Jill Bennett

ISBN 1 4052 0467 2

10 9 8 7 6 5 4 3 2 1

A CIP catalogue record for this title is available from the British Library.

Printed and bound in Great Britain by Cox & Wyman Ltd, Reading, Berkshire

Contents

An interview with
Michelle Magorian
by Kate Agnew

Michelle Magorian's Books

Michelle Magorian (b. 1948) worked in theatre, television and film, before becoming a highly-acclaimed children's author. Her first book, Goodnight Mister Tom, *won many awards, including the Guardian Children's Fiction Award, was made into a captivating film for television (Bafta, 1998), and regularly appears on school reading lists and is published in ten different languages. Her other titles include* Back Home *(winner of the American Library Association Award and the West Australian Young Readers Book Award),* A Little Love Song, Cuckoo in the Nest *and* A Spoonful of Jam.

Michelle's latest book is a collection of short stories called Be Yourself.

An interview with

Michelle Magorian

by Kate Agnew

My childhood home

Where were you born?

Southsea, Hampshire.

What was the nearest town and what did you like best about it?

Portsmouth. In my late teens I used any excuse to go into the King's Theatre there. It was a large Victorian theatre; Henry Irving and Ellen Terry performed in it. I even sneaked into the auditorium and sat in the dark watching a new company set up. They had pre-London shows. I saw Neil Simon's *Barefoot in the Park* with

Daniel Massey and *The Prime of Miss Jean Brodie* starring Vanessa Redgrave. Although painfully shy, it was a wonderful refuge for me. It's still there.

Who did you get on with best?

I got on with both my brothers. I was both very bossy towards and very protective of them.

Were any animals part of the household?

My brother Jeremy once had a pet bantam, but it kept waking the neighbours at five am so we drove out to a farm and left it there. Then he had an aviary but a cat got into it. He was so devastated he wanted to have the dead birds stuffed.

We had the odd visiting cat, which we had to shoo off as my mother was terrified of them!

In Singapore, where I lived from the age of three months to three, I had a dog called Chunky, who used to sleep under my cot, but I can't remember him.

* * *

My family

What did your family consist of?

Mother, Father, two brothers, Jeremy and Simon, born when I was five and ten-years-old. (And, briefly, Lee Kim who looked after me when I was a baby and toddler.)

Michelle (left), Jeremy, and their cousins in Ireland.

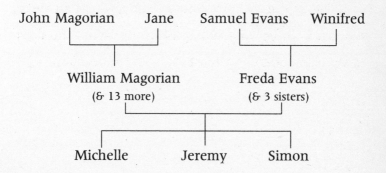

John Magorian   Jane   Samuel Evans   Winifred

William Magorian   Freda Evans
(& 13 more)   (& 3 sisters)

Michelle   Jeremy   Simon

Did your grandparents play any part in your family?

My Irish grandmother died of TB after giving birth to her ninth child in fourteen years. My father was the eldest – he was fourteen. My grandfather then had five more children by a second wife. Aged ten to eighteen, I saw my Irish grandfather for two weeks a year and I have lovely memories of him.

My Welsh grandfather died when I was a baby. I have 'inherited' some of his traits: an unconventional clergyman, he loved Shakespeare, Dickens and Tolstoy and worked on his sermons by pacing up and down. We saw my granny on Sundays. She used to give wonderful high teas with Welsh cakes, ginger and chocolate cake. She had long white hair with a blonde streak in it and collected rainwater in a bucket to wash it in. She used to wear it in a bun. It was fascinating to watch her do it. She had a place for everything and everything in its place, but the order made a refreshing break from the chaos of home.

Was your childhood happy?

I had some wonderful times and some unhappy

nightmarish times. Aged ten to eighteen was the worst.

What is your best memory of it?

Wandering around an empty local theatre which was booked for our annual dance performances – I'd arrive with my costumes in a suitcase well before anyone else arrived and drink it all in. Sleeping in a tent and listening to the rain pattering on the flysheet, warm inside my sleeping bag. Listening to one of my friends play the piano. Hanging around the King's Theatre in Southsea. Saturday morning cinema in Australia (aged nine). Seeing snow on our sloping rooftops in the middle of the night. I had a friend staying over and my father must have taken it for granted that we would still be awake. He got us out of bed and lifted us up through the skylight window and it was magical.

I also have memories of standing on my father's feet and him dancing with me. My father had a wonderful singing voice. He'd sing old Irish ballads and Victorian songs. I loved hearing him sing. I wished he'd sing more often. I loved hearing my mother laugh. She would cry at the same time. It was so infectious that it would have other people collapsing around her and it would escalate so that I'd beg her to stop because I'd be laughing so much that it hurt.

The other thing I liked was my mother 'finishing off' dramas on the television. If it was one which left you in the air she'd say that this was going to happen to one of the characters and they would meet such and such, and then, etc... She would always take the time to listen to my stories and if the teachers gave me low marks for them she'd tell me that I deserved more!

What is your worst memory of it?

Hiding in my bedroom when I was ten-years-old and looking after my brother who was five as we listened to the shouting and crashing downstairs. Then my father calling me out and him standing at the foot of the stairs telling me my pregnant mother was going to stay with my granny and demanding who I was going to go with, her or him. And when I was too stunned, numb and in pain to answer, he yelled at my brother and told him that everything his grandfather had told him was a lie and that there was no such thing as fairies, or Father Christmas. And I remember taking my sobbing brother back into the bedroom and holding him, deciding I

Michelle's parents.

wouldn't have either of them and that I would look after Jeremy and keep the family together that way. I became middle-aged in seconds; I caught up with my childhood later though!

What made you sad?

The last day of the summer term, knowing I had two months at home to get through.

What were your first words?

My first words were, 'The boys were very rough,

weren't they', aged three years, when my father was tucking me up in bed. I hadn't said one word before then and my parents had been worrying.

*   *   *

My schooldays

What was your first school like?

Very caring, it was the junior part of a convent. I went to two schools in Australia. (We lived there from when I was seven to when I was nine-and-a-half.) I had nightmares at the first and was moved to Kilbreda College in Mentone where I did very well but was a little naughty.

Who was your favourite teacher?

My dance teachers and elocution teacher, and a young visiting teacher who brought history alive.

Who was your most hated teacher?

I didn't have one.

When did you learn to read? Was it hard?

I can't remember, but I won a reading prize when I was five. I picked it up very quickly.

What was your secondary school like?

Wonderful; a convent school in the country with nuns who loved us and nurtured our individual talents.

What was your favourite subject?

Drama and English.

What was your most hated subject?

Geography.

Who was your favourite teacher there?

Mrs Kent; in Form 1 she called me her dormouse because I seemed to wake up in the summer term.

What was your best subject?

English.

What was your worst subject?

Geography.

What was your handwriting like then?

Like now; swings from indecipherable to neat.

This way, and that, she peers, and sees.
silver fruit upon silver trees; ✓

21ˢᵗ May. 1958.

Composition.

One day as the twins were walking across
the park they noticed a very old house It
looked weird and spooky. The twins who
loved adventure decided to explore it that
night. When they went to bed Simon one
of the twins put an alarm clock under his
pillow and set the alarm for 12 o, clock it
was 1 minute to 12 now, the alarm went
off. Simon scrambled out of bed and was

Michelle's handwriting.

Did any teacher think you might become a writer?

I think Miss Quinn – my geography teacher!

What are your first memories of reading?

Being frightened by my reading prize, *The Tale Of Samuel Whiskers*. I remember breaking out into a sweat the first time I read it to my elder son.

What did reading mean to you?

Escape and, later, discovery.

What did words mean to you?

Access to a world outside my own and insights into areas where I was confused.

Were you shy or talkative, solitary or sociable?

All four, still am!

Who was your favourite children's author?

Enid Blyton, Arthur Ransome.

When did you start reading adult authors?

Aged about sixteen; plays by Terrence Rattigan, the poems of Wilfred Owen and I loved Neil Simon. The war poets had a tremendous effect on me. When I was a student, someone introduced me to Tolstoy and I went head over heels. I remember walking on my own in Paris in the snow and imagining I was in Russia. I also loved plays. I read *Barefoot in the Park* by Neil Simon in the library and had to leave I was laughing so much. When I went to college I had a craze for American playwrights, Arthur Miller, Tennessee Williams. I would save up my grant money so that I could go and see a matinée.

Did you read poetry?

Yes, World War I poets and, later, the Liverpool poets.

Did you read non-fiction?

Yes, psychology and Stanislavski.

What was your favourite non-fiction book?

Tricky! In my teens, *An Actor Prepares* or *Preparing A Character* by Stanislavski, and a tiny 1930s' book on introducing psychology including full explanations of introversion, extroversion, regression, etc.

What sport did you like?

Trampolining.

What sport do you enjoy now?

Swimming, going to the gym (if I get the chance!)

What music did you listen to?

Musicals, popular classics, the Beatles and pop music.

Was music important to you then?

Yes.

Is it now?

Yes.

What music do you listen to now?

Stephen Sondheim's and other musicals, some classical.

Did you enjoy painting?

Yes, but hardly did any at all.

Do you enjoy painting now, or looking at paintings?

I like looking at paintings. I really admire the ability to draw.

What part did cinema, drama and television play in your life then?

A lot.

What part do they play now?

I don't have much time as a single mother; I haven't been to the cinema in years, but I've started going to the theatre again.

Who was your favourite film or TV star then?

Jerry Lewis – he made me laugh when I was eight or nine.

Who is your favourite now?

Judi Dench.

What is your favourite film?

I Know Where I'm Going, a 1940s' black and white film with a very young Wendy Hillier.

*   *   *

My career

What did you do when you left school?

My further education was at: The Rose Bruford College of Speech and Drama, 1966–1969, and at L'école Internationale de Mime, Marcel Marceau in Paris, 1969–1970. Getting into Drama schools when I was eighteen was pretty wonderful. I got into three. I didn't audition for any more after that. Two of them accepted me at the audition. The first time it happened I rang my mother and after I had told her she said, 'You mean they're going to write to you?' and I said, 'No! I've been offered a place now!' My parents weren't keen on the idea of me going into the theatre but after that they had to give in.

What was your first job?

Rumplestiltskin for the Argyl Theatre for Youth.

Why did you decide to do it?

It was touring (I had itchy feet), it was my first Equity

contract (difficult to get), and it was a big part.

How long did you stay in it?

For the autumn.

What did you do next and why?

There was a job waiting for me at the Q20 Theatre Company in Yorkshire. It was a wonderful opportunity not only to act, but to write dialogue and songs, to sing

Michelle in 'Patches', her mime show.

Michelle (left) in 'Rookery Nook' at Perth Theatre.

and to leap around. There were lots of wonderful talented people in the company and we did everything – sewing, painting – a huge variety of work.

After my contract finished in the summer I was offered a year's work with the Orchard Theatre Company in Devon. Again, it was a chance to do an enormous variety of roles in a touring company which lived and worked together in a very committed and caring way.

I then stopped touring. I suddenly wanted to stay put. I was offered a job at a repertory company where I only had to act! I continued working in repertory theatre in Perth, Newcastle, Leeds, Birmingham, Worcester, Northampton, Basingstoke, Watford Palace Theatre,

Michelle preparing for her role as the Monkey Wife.

Windsor Palace Theatre, Shaftesbury Theatre, the Young Vic, Colchester. I did half musicals and half plays, acting 'character' parts and leaning towards comedy.

I also did my quota of hairy creatures, Orinoco Womble, Paddington Bear and the Monkey Wife in the musical of that name.

*   *   *

My career as a writer

Did you write as a child?

Yes – stories. While I was training to become an actress I wrote masses of very sad poetry, and some funny poems for special occasions like people's birthdays.

When did you decide to become a professional writer?

In my thirties, I joined a novel-writing class and the tutor Dulan Barber, who was also a writer, persuaded me to send my manuscript of *Goodnight Mister Tom* to the agent Pat White, who loved it and sent it to a publisher.

How and when did you start to write?

In 1970, scripts and lyrics in Q20. I carried on writing odd lyrics and poetry and I kept journals and dream diaries, and wrote short stories and a novella. I also wrote a couple of plays at college.

Where did you get your idea for your first novel?

Goodnight Mister Tom began as one of a set of ten stories about colours, based on a song from *Joseph and the Amazing Technicolour Dreamcoat*. I was sitting in the launderette thinking about the colours green and brown, and I began to think of leaves and trees. Brown made me think of earthiness and stability and green made me think of youth and vulnerability. I thought of a young beech tree with a slim trunk and suddenly I saw a picture in my head of a small, thin, frightened boy standing in a graveyard. I knew he was an evacuee because he had a label. He became William Beech.

My mother had been a nurse during the war. I remembered her telling me two stories, one about a boy who curled up under the hospital bed; he had never slept in a bed before. The other was about a boy whose underwear had been sewn together. His mother was furious when she realised that my mother had unpicked all the stitches.

The tenth story in the collection was about the paint box that Tom Oakley had hidden in his cupboard. I wrote about Tom and his young wife Rachel and their

Michelle's mother in her Q.A. uniform.

idyllic days together. I couldn't get William Beech and Tom Oakley out of my head, I wanted to know what happened to them next. I spent years working on it and I couldn't contain my excitement when it was finished, but even then I had no intention of sending it to a publisher until I read a chapter of it aloud at my novel-writing class and the tutor persuaded me to send it off.

Where did your next novels come from?

Once I started researching for *Goodnight Mister Tom* there were so many more questions I wanted to ask. I came across a photograph of a group of English children on a liner returning to England after living in America for five years. I remembered the problem I had had returning to England after just two-and-a-half years in

Australia. And these children had been separated from their parents. The photograph wouldn't go away and eventually it became the beginning of *Back Home*.

I was born after the terrible winter of 1947 and I suppose I wanted to go back and find out more about the period. There is a theory that some people like writing about the time just before they were born. The period chose me really.

I'm interested in the theatre in the 1940s; people who were working then are still alive and I wanted to bring it back to life. I met a director who had started by doing odd jobs for the theatre. He'd been evacuated for five years and wanted to stay in the country. He wanted to be a farmer but his father insisted on bringing him back. He started doing an apprenticeship and in the evenings he did work for the local variety theatre. It got into his blood and he was hooked. He ended up being head of drama at a university. That was the seed of *Cuckoo in the Nest*.

When I came to *A Spoonful of Jam*, I wanted to develop the characters more. I wanted to know more about the incident where Elsie had to be rescued, and I came across an interview with a grammar school girl who went hop-picking. She had to leave early to go back to school, unlike her cousins, and she didn't really feel part of either life. I was fascinated too by the cold winter of 1947 and the hot summer that came after it, when I was born. I researched the weather; one time I went into a newspaper library and just looked at weather forecasts. It was a mosaic really; I started to daydream little bits here and little bits there.

Who encouraged or dissuaded you?

My mother liked to hear my stories. My teachers, however, were not so keen. One teacher used to tell me off for writing stories.

What, if any, writer influenced you?

I don't know if he influenced me, but I admired him – Tolstoy. Even when a minor character appears only on one page he seems able to make them a fully-rounded person and so vivid. One can see them scratching their nose and leaning against a mantelpiece. But I love Neil Simon too, and Ayckbourn and Michael Frayn. I love Michael Frayn's stuff; he's funny and intellectual as well.

Do you like being a writer?

Yes.

What do you like best about writing?

Writing dialogue.

Can you help being a writer?

No.

Is it an obsession or compulsion?

Compulsion.

Is it a lonely profession?

No, because you have the company of your fictional people and you meet people when carrying out research.

Do you find writing hard?

I have excruciatingly difficult days, and days when I can't write fast enough for my thoughts.

Did you start with habits that you've since changed?

Can't think of any.

How long does it take to write a book?

If I'm not doing anything else, two years. *Goodnight Mister Tom* took me four years – three years to write the first draft, a year to re-write it. During the first three years I was writing it, I was also working in repertory theatre which involves working six days and six nights a week, rehearsing one play during the day, performing another at night. I wrote on Sundays and in between acting jobs. *A Little Love Song* took six to seven years from start to finish, but for two or three years of that time it was in the loft.

Do you have any rituals that you do before writing?

Scribbling a few notes.

'No' he had said simply. (you

boy. Turned up at seventeen. Eighty years ago...

And Elsie noticed than when up...
~~adult rising by prickly head down again~~.
'Schoolboy. Soldier. Labourer.
Life so far' She laughed.

On ~~Easter~~ ~~Holy~~ Friday ~~even~~
~~as last week~~ to a Whitbread farm
she had heard th group of actors a
actresses would be performing Twelf
Night.
~~It was~~ there ~~were~~ ~~no chairs~~
sat on the grass and watched the
actors dart about, ~~way their~~ ...
and so only there!

'I don't understand a bleedin' wor
this! She heard a woman mutter
to her ~~again Elsie didn't~~ understood it
either didn't...

Malvolia ~~who~~ ...
...plays a underplo
~~...make...believe~~
in love with him. Wha she wa
lying about the yellow stockings ad
cross garter Malcolm his legs.

Olivia the actress Dostny ~~speaks a~~
~~...~~ heard at the stage
amorous prayer about ad Dostny
the ~~...~~ ...
...stage phrase
more ~~...~~ Elsie's scalp tingle, as...
magic had brushed her with th
unseen, so it was wet sit t

342

Is there a pattern to the writing day?

Not since having children.

Do you rewrite?

Lots.

When your story is finished, who reads your manuscript first?

I used to read it aloud to my ex-husband. Also, I hand it over to a young person in case some of my research background is too obscure.

Do you listen to criticism?

Yes. I also disagree with it sometimes.

Why do you write for children?

I'm not sure why I write for children. Maybe I like looking at life through a young person's eyes. Perhaps I want to articulate what they're feeling. I'm not sure.

An example of Michelle's redrafting.

Where do your ideas come from?

Ideas come from photos, questions I want answered, overheard snippets of conversation, daydreams.

What subjects appeal to you?

Relationships between people and how they affect one another.

What kind of research do you do?

Reading, interviews, newspapers, films.

How important is imagination?

Vital.

Do you base your situations on real life?

Not consciously.

Do you base your characters on real people?

No, but real people have sometimes snuck in.

What matters most - the story or the characters?

The characters. Their relationships with one another create the story.

Who do you write for?

Me.

Which of your books is your favourite?

I don't have one.

Which is your favourite character in your own books?

Zach, Charlie, Elsie, Jessica, Rose, Miss Hilda, Dot – I have many favourites.

Are pictures important in your books?

I write mostly for older children who I hope can create pictures from my words.

What gives you most satisfaction about being a writer?

I love getting lost in another situation and having the dialogue between the characters taking off, almost out of my control, and being surprised with what they come out with.

What do you dislike most about writing?

Sitting.

What do you hope to achieve with your books?

I want to connect readers with different kinds of people; I want readers to enjoy and care about the people I've invented, to be carried away by the story, to be watching a film in their heads.

Why is fiction important?

Fiction is important because it expands people's boundaries. It makes people feel less isolated when they can connect with the people they're reading about.

Will it still be important in the new century?

Of course.

Do you think TV can complement reading or be a substitute for it?

Complement.

Which book, either children's or adult, has influenced your life?

So many books have influenced my life; Tolstoy's *Anna Karenina*, *Six Bad Boys* by Enid Blyton and Arthur Ransome's *Swallows and Amazons*.

Which book comforts you most?

At the moment, *Life and How to Survive It* by John Cleese and Robin Skinner.

Michelle's Christmas thank you letter, aged fifteen.

Cover artwork by Jessica Meserve for *A Little Love Song*

Michelle's Books

An overview by Kate Agnew

WHEN *Goodnight Mister Tom* was published in 1981, it met with immediate and widespread critical acclaim from adults and children alike, and Michelle Magorian was quickly established as a leading contemporary children's writer. Winner of the Guardian Children's Fiction Award and now regularly appearing on school reading lists, *Goodnight Mister Tom* remains enormously popular and is published in ten different languages. The story of an abused child who escapes his brutal home life when he is evacuated to the countryside during World War II, it displays all the characteristics for which Michelle's work is now well-known and loved. William Beech is unloved, uncared for and uneducated when he arrives in Little Weirwold, while Mister Tom, to whose home he is sent because his mother has insisted that he must be in sight of a church, appears a surly old man, made bitter by the untimely death of his wife and child many years before. The story that unfolds is one of love, friendship, patience and hard work.

Further novels

Since 1981, Michelle has published a further four novels, two picture books, two volumes of poetry and a number of short stories. The novels, for which she is best known, form part of a long tradition of writing for children in which family love, personal integrity and strong moral values are seen as central to the development of the main characters. The 'family' may not be the traditional family unit for William Beech any more than it is for Anne of Green Gables, but for both the need for stability and a happy home is paramount.

Michelle's characters come to understand that it is not material things that create happiness. In *Cuckoo in the Nest* and *A Spoonful of Jam*, Ralph and Elsie Hollis, living in a cramped and overcrowded house are upset by their poverty only because it marks them out as different from their grammar school contemporaries. What really upsets them is their father's refusal to acknowledge the things that matter to them. In *Back Home*, Rusty initially misses her comfortable American lifestyle but comes to realise that it is not the physical comforts of smart clothes or central heating for which she longs, but the pleasure of being part of a large and loving family.

Believe in yourself . . .

In *Back Home*, as Rusty faces life with an unfamiliar family in a strange land, her adopted family offers her a set of rules by which to live her life: 'Believe in yourself,' they tell her, 'believe in others, and work like hell.' These instructions provide a set of values for all Michelle's characters as they confront the complex and changing world of Britain in the 1940s.

Self-belief does not come easily to the heroes and heroines of Michelle's novels. Even characters like Ralph Hollis or Rusty, who appear initially to be brimming with self-confidence, have to go through a difficult period of change before they can begin to be sure of their own position. Self-confidence can only be secured within a loving home and each has to resolve their family problems before they can be certain of themselves.

At the beginning of *Back Home*, Rusty is a happy and chatty girl, sure of her own opinions and secure in the love of her adopted American family. Dressed in her American teenagers' clothes she arrives back in Britain nervous but confident, asking her mother questions and talking about art and the theatre. Her confidence unnerves her mother who last encountered 'Rusty' – or Virginia as she prefers to call her – as a quiet, spindly-legged small child. Similarly, Ralph's father cannot understand the differences in his son since he left home and went to live in a Cornish vicarage. For both Rusty and Ralph their parents' absence during their childhood and subsequent lack of understanding deals a severe blow to their self-confidence.

Parent trouble

The irony for both Ralph and Rusty is that their differences with their parents stem in part from their similarities. Mr Hollis acknowledges Ralph's inherited stubbornness with a degree of pride, while Rusty's mother finally joins Rusty in a truly independent life.

Both Rusty's father and Mr Hollis have been absent for a long time. Their return to family life is made especially difficult as they have just spent several years largely in the company of men. Mr Hollis loathes Ralph's 'Nancy boy' interest in the theatre, and neither father knows how to respond to his young daughter. Elsie recognises this and blames her sex. She is certain that her father would take pride in her and invite her to join him and Harry at the allotment – an invitation for which she longs – if only she was a boy. Finally she resorts to cutting her hair and dressing as a boy, but her father still doesn't seem to understand her.

World War II

All Michelle's novels are set during World War II and its aftermath. The period provides a powerful vehicle for the exploration of the changing nature of human relationships and the importance of family love and lasting friendship. Fathers have been absent from family life and women have learned new skills and independence, while children have grown up more quickly than their parents realise, straining the limits of family tolerance. Although the loving family is seen as the base from which each character can establish his or her own identity, the war has driven families apart. In each of the novels there is a marked tension between the image of happy family life for which the characters strive and the reality that confronts the young heroes and heroines as they struggle to establish their own identity, while those around them piece together their lives against a backdrop of war, poverty and hardship.

In Michelle's work the war allows a degree of independence that would never before have been possible, particularly for young women; for Rusty it means evacuation to America where the term 'teenager' has just been coined, and to a family free from the conventions of British society. For Rose and Diana in *A Little Love Song*, it brings a chance to plan their own lives away from the conventions that would otherwise restrict them. Rose, especially, gains the intellectual freedom to develop her writing and plan a future career.

For William Beech, the war offers an opportunity to escape from the cruelty of his home life and to begin afresh with Mister Tom. None of Michelle's characters is more lacking in self-belief than William when he first arrives, sewn into his underwear for the winter and covered in bruises. But William flourishes under Mister Tom's tender care to become an integral part of his life, filling the gap that was left when his own child died. The link between love and self-confidence is made even more obvious when William returns to London and to his mother. The cruelty he experiences at his mother's hands is both shocking and disturbing.

When the book was adapted for television in 1998, it was shown as an adult film, after the nine o'clock watershed.

Independent women

One senses that, whenever the novels had been set, Michelle's heroines would have been strong independent women, but for all her women, young and old alike, the war brings the possibility of escape from routine domestic duties and a chance to demonstrate their skill outside the home. Rusty's mother has not only learned to drive and to fix cars, but has also found the independence necessary to leave her restrictive life and her old-fashioned husband, abandoning the values of her mother-in-law and setting up her own home. Rusty, like her mother, has to learn that life has changed for every generation and that her mother, too, deserves her independence.

However, the lifestyle of women who choose to stay at home and care for their families is shown to be as important as that of their colleagues who go out to work. Ralph and Elsie's Aunty Win has clearly flourished during her time in the WAAF and feels oppressed and undervalued when she returns home. She tries to encourage Ralph's mother to leave her family and join up, but Ralph takes his mum to a play celebrating the lives of women who have stayed at home caring for their families. For the women as well as the men in Michelle's novels, it is freedom of choice and the independence this brings that matter as much as the choices they eventually make.

A loving relationship

The war, however, is shown to have changed society's view of women irrevocably. The greatest social change of all is seen in Dot (*A Little Love Song*). Pregnant but unmarried, Dot's story mirrors that of Hilda, a woman who was in the same situation more than twenty years earlier, during World War I. Each had been in love with the dead father of their unborn child, but for Hilda their physical relationship led her own father to lock her away in a mental asylum, while for Dot life will be manageable if she can only afford a pretend wedding ring.

Unlike many children's novelists, Michelle sees sex as an integral part of a happy loving relationship, and not something which should be condemned outside marriage. It is not, however, a necessary part of any friendship between boy and girl. When Rusty returns from America, she is used to talking to boys as equals, knows the facts of life and is quite happy to have a friendship with a boy that is entirely platonic. For Rusty, Lance can both replace the family from whom she is becoming increasingly detached, and represent the America of her dreams. Her mother, however, is clearly horrified when she speaks to a boy, while her school is shocked that she should even think of addressing a boy in public. The other girls believe that Rusty could have got herself pregnant merely by being with a boy in her pyjamas.

Curiosity and even disgust about sex are seen to be entirely natural. Ralph is appalled at the prospect of his parents sleeping together and is visibly embarrassed at his mother's pregnancy, but when Isla comes back from the Isle of Wight, where she has been snowed in with her new husband, Ralph is eager to discover whether she appears any different. Rose avidly reads Dot's pregnancy book in order to become better informed, and her knowledge turns out to be essential when Dot goes into labour.

For the young heroes of Michelle's novels, the boundaries between friendship and first love are often blurred. In *A Little Love Song*, Rose initially views Alec as a good friend, someone far too old to be considered romantically. For Ralph Hollis, Jessica Egerton-Smythe is first a good friend; being obsessed with Isla he does not think of Jessica as a girlfriend until he comes to realise how much he misses her in her absence. Even then he still seems to play the role of a son in the family. Mrs Egerton-Smythe and Jessica mother him together, giving him the clothes that once belonged to Jessica's dead brother and encouraging him to start his own theatre wardrobe. The shift from brotherly love to romantic feeling is so gradual that even Ralph himself has to seek clarification from Jessica, needing to know for sure how she feels about him.

For all the main characters friendship is as important as sex in a happy relationship; Alec and Rose, like Jessica and Ralph, are friends before they become lovers. For Rose, sex without love is a nightmare. Its clinical quality reminds her of an operation, but with Alec whom she loves, the experience is quite different; rather than feeling like a sacrificial lamb she feels herself 'dissolving into a delicious whirlpool'.

The support of friends and family

Rose and Alec's physical happiness mirrors their intellectual partnership. Alec is interested in books, writes himself and understands Rose's ambition to be a writer. Rose's relationship with Derry is unsatisfactory not least because Derry has no interest in Rose's work or in her inner world. In marked contrast, Alec not only encourages her to write, but is responsible for her first publication, developing her self-confidence and believing in what she can do. It is this intertwining of self-belief and others' belief in their abilities that gives all the characters their inner strength and conviction. All are on the verge of adulthood, struggling to establish their own independence while longing for the strength, comfort and certainty offered by family and friends.

In the absence of family affection it is often friends who provide moral support and comfort. For William, Mister Tom becomes a second father, and for Ralph and Elsie the theatre provides a second home and an extended family. Mrs Egerton-Smythe also plays a vital role in the development of Ralph's career in the theatre. Although nominally Ralph's employer, she not only provides props for the plays, houses members of the cast and allows him time off work to act, but more importantly she provides the advice and encouragement that Ralph's family cannot.

Although Ralph, like Rusty in *Back Home*, feels initially let down by his family and better supported by his friends, both Ralph and Rusty still feel a strong need for their families to believe in them and accept them for what they are. They have to learn to compromise if they want to be accepted by both family and friends. Although Ralph's father will never be happy that his son has picked the stage for a career, his intense dislike of the theatre is softened when he discovers that Ralph's acting hero is an old army friend. He even ends up acting himself, despite his fear of what his friends might say. For Rusty, too, compromises must be made; her father will never understand her desire for freedom and her failure to conform, but eventually Rusty learns that her mother's approval and understanding are enough.

Humour

The books deal with powerful emotions and difficult issues – family separations, wartime losses, abuse and neglect – yet all of Michelle's novels exhibit their author's irrepressible sense of humour. We cannot help but laugh at Aunty Win's ghoulish and enthusiastic response to news of murder or – even better – suicide in the newspaper, while Ralph's struggle to carry a stuffed life-sized bear down the busy streets of Winford is unforgettable.

Perhaps most memorable of all is the scene in *A Little Love Song* where Rose, out at her first dance but suddenly determined to do her bit towards household economy, fills her capacious bloomers with leftover orange peel, bent on making marmalade. However, as she jitterbugs around the dance floor, the elastic of her ancient, heavy black knickers finally gives way to shower her – and everyone around her – with orange peel. Rose is appalled but for the reader – as for the appreciative GIs – it is a moment of high comedy.

Theatre

Michelle's characters all share their author's love of acting and the theatre. Against the backdrop of the 1940s, the theatre represents a means of escape from the humdrum world of blackouts, rationing and wartime regulations. For both Ralph and Elsie the theatre offers a taste of the adult world, a chance to make new friends and to enter into a new lifestyle.

Although Ralph is initially an outsider in the world of the theatre, lacking either the money or the training to qualify him for the job he wants, he is quickly accepted and valued for the work he does, rapidly becoming part of the large and supportive theatre family who share in his passions and interests.

The theatre possesses almost magical qualities, liberating him from everyday worries and offering friendship, moral support and, eventually, paid work and a career. For Elsie it is even more magical, removing her from all her problems at one fell swoop with an undreamed of offer of a major part and a protector who helps her to overcome her shyness and fear of being bullied.

Even William Beech demonstrates his growing self-confidence as he progresses from reluctant prompter to actor in his own right. William is able to overcome his shyness as he pretends to be a different person, but for Elsie Hollis, used to acting a part both at school and at home, the joy of being in the theatre is that it allows her to be herself. On her return to school her experience in the theatre paves the way for her to be accepted by her contemporaries and her teachers.

Education

Ralph and Elsie gain access to the world of the theatre because of their education; their grammar school background allows them to cut across class divides – though it is this same education which leads to Elsie being bullied and Ralph being mistrusted by his father. For all the characters, education is of vital importance, and is often seen as the first step towards allowing them to grow away from their social and family background.

William Beech appears to have received no education at all when he comes to Little Weirwold, and the teaching Mister Tom gives him is almost as important as the love and affection. For William, learning to read means not just acquiring a new skill, but gaining the freedom to join his friends in his rightful classroom.

For Rusty, too, education is equated with both happiness and independence. In America she was a bright and happy child who did well at school, but in Britain she is viewed as stupid since she knows nothing of British history, Latin or algebra, and speaks always in what her contemporaries regard as 'slang'. Michelle satirises the world of the girls' boarding school, which allows no space for individuality of expression and cares less for educating its girls than for producing 'young women who would make good wives and mothers'. Bereft of both education and family love, Rusty feels abandoned and isolated, living only for the time when she can escape to the derelict cottage and be herself.

Happiness at a price

Rusty eventually finds happiness when she returns to the country and moves to a school where pupils are encouraged to think and act independently. Rusty has to pay a price for independence, however; the house they love has become their own only because of the death of a beloved friend and, in choosing to live with her mother, Rusty incurs her father's extreme displeasure and his threat to 'cut them all off without a penny'. For all Michelle's heroes and heroines, happiness demands a high price. They not only have to work hard, but must be prepared to make sacrifices in order to achieve happiness eventually. For the reader, however, it is this very struggle that makes their eventual happiness so appealing. The world of Michelle's books is not that of a fairy-tale land where everyone can expect to live happily ever after, but a captivating and believable world in which hard work and determination, coupled with the desire to love and to be loved, can finally bring characters the happiness they deserve.

Kate Agnew

1999

Bibliography
In date order

Goodnight Mister Tom

Kestrel Books 1981

William Beech is evacuated to the country to live with Tom Oakley at the start of World War II. A lonely child, he finds care and comfort with the surly old man.

Winner of the Guardian Children's Fiction Award 1981, the International Reading Association Children's Book Award 1982 and the West Australian Young Readers Book Award; runner-up for the 1981 Young Observer Award; Shortlisted for the Carnegie Book Award.

BAFTA Award-winning TV film, 1998

Back Home

Viking 1985

When Virginia ('Rusty') is sent back to live in England after being evacuated to America during the war, she finds Britain a poverty-stricken and depressing place where even her own family seem strangers. Gradually, she learns to think of the strange country as home and begins to understand the way of life there.

Winner of the American Library Association Best Book for Young Adults 1984 and the West Australian Young Readers Book Award
TV Film 1989, screenplay by David Wood
Dramatised for BBC Radio 4

Waiting For My Shorts To Dry

Viking 1989, illustrated by Jean Baylis
A collection of poems for young children published in picture book format with colour illustrations.

Who's Going To Take Care Of Me?

Harper & Row, US 1990, illustrated by James Graham Hale

Orange Paw Marks

Viking 1991, illustrated by Jean Baylis

A collection of poems based on events children will recognise from their own experience.

A Little Love Song

Methuen 1991, Mammoth 1998

In 1943, seventeen-year-old Rose and her older sister Diana are sent to a seemingly-sleepy village to keep them out of harm's way. When their chaperone fails to turn up, the two girls experience their first taste of independence and Rose finds herself falling in love for the first time.

Jump

Walker 1992, illustrated by Jan Ormerod

A picture book about a boy who wants to dance although his mother wants him to play basketball.

In Deep Water

Viking 1992

A collection of short stories about water and the sea.

Cuckoo In The Nest

Methuen 1994

During World War II, Ralph has been evacuated to a Cornish vicarage where he has acquired an accent and a way of life that his father cannot understand. Ralph wants to pursue a career in the theatre, but his father is equally convinced that the theatre is only for sissies. Ralph's father is horrified when Ralph loses his respectable job at the mill, but Ralph is determined to find work at the theatre.

A Spoonful Of Jam

Methuen 1998

Ralph's younger sister Elsie feels an outsider everywhere. At school her accent isn't posh enough, on the streets she is bullied for being a grammar school girl, and at home her father cannot understand her love of books and reading. It is only when she visits Ralph at the theatre that she discovers a way of resolving her difficulties.

Be Yourself

Egmont 2003

An inspirational collection of short stories about learning to trust your own identity.

Short Stories

'The Front Room' in *They Wait and Other Stories*

Pepper Press 1983

Compiled by Lance Salway, illustrated by Jill Bennett

'Beginners' in *Guardian Angels*

Viking Kestrel 1987

Compiled by Stephanie Nettell, illustrated by Mike Daley

'The Greatest' in *You're Late Dad*

Methuen Children's Books 1989

Edited by Tony Bradman

'The Smile' in *Love Them, Hate Them*

Methuen Children's Books 1991

Edited by Tony Bradman

'Whiting' in *Stage Struck*

Hamish Hamilton 1991

Edited by Jean Richardson

Scripts

You and Me

BBC Schools television

Sea Change

with Stephen Keeling & Peter Venner, 1998

The Front Room

Michelle Magorian

Helen woke up sharply. Face to the wall, she felt again that horrifying presence behind her. She took a deep breath, gritted her teeth, and forced herself to look round. In the semi-darkness shadows moved. She pushed herself quickly out of bed, sprinted across the room and turned on the light.

All she could see was her bed up by the window, a faded sofa, two armchairs, a shabby carpet, and a table and two chairs up against the wall by the door. Even so, she decided to keep the light on. Her parents would be furious if she woke them up a fourth night running. When she had dashed into their room the previous night, their patience had finally snapped.

'There's absolutely nothing wrong with that room,' her mother had said. 'You're acting like a baby.

Anybody would think you were two instead of eleven.'

'You know your mother needs a good rest,' said her father. 'If I have any more of this nonsense, I'll stop your pocket money.'

Helen had clambered quickly back into bed. She needed that pocket money desperately. For over a year she had been saving up for a guitar. Her father had even promised that if she helped out and did some baby-sitting he'd pay her proper baby-sitting rates as well.

'Couldn't I sleep with Brian?' she had suggested. Her three-year-old brother slept at the end of the corridor in a small room which led into the kitchen.

'There's not enough room,' her mother had said crossly. 'It's only a divan.'

'But Mum –' Helen had protested.

'Now belt up,' her father had said, 'or I'll give you a good hiding.'

Her parents weren't usually so bad-tempered, but ever since Mum had lost the baby they always seemed to be quarrelling.

Helen pulled the curtains aside and stared out at the dark street below. They had been lucky to find this holiday flat at all, and the old woman who owned the place had gone out of her way to put a bed into the front room for Helen.

As soon as the dawn came, Helen felt it was safe enough to go back to sleep. She had hardly closed her eyes when she was being woken up by her father.

'Did you sleep with the light on all night?' he said angrily.

'No, Dad, only a bit of it. I didn't want to wake you up.' Her father sat on the bed. He was a big man with a round nose and untidy brown hair. Helen, though small, was the spitting image of him.

'Look, kiddo.' He always called her that when he treated her special. 'What's up?'

She pushed herself up onto her elbows. 'I don't know. One minute I'm asleep and then I wake up and I can feel someone in the room.'

Her father gazed awkwardly at his hands. 'Look,' he said, 'I know me and your mum haven't been getting on too well lately. That's because we're tired and we're a bit upset because of the baby. You know.'

'Yeah.'

'We're just going through a bad patch, that's all. Your mum's already looking a bit perkier. The sea air's cheering her up. I know it's not much of a holiday for you, but if you could just keep on looking after Brian, it'd make a lot of difference.'

Helen sat up, puzzled. 'But you know I'm happy to do that, Dad.'

And it was true. Looking after Brian, so that her parents could go off together, made her feel useful, important.

'I thought maybe you were a bit fed up of being left with him and were trying to get your own back.'

'Dad!'

'I just wanted to make sure,' he said, standing up. 'I'll get breakfast going, eh?' And he gave a broad grin.

Helen grinned back and pushed the bedclothes aside.

Her first job in the morning was to wash and dress Brian. Mum had breakfast in bed on a tray. Dad had refused to let her get up for breakfast all through the holiday. That morning, she and Brian stuck a little bunch of flowers in an empty fish-paste pot filled with water, and her father placed it on the tray and carried it in to her mother. After eating breakfast with them, he took a mug of tea into the bedroom while Helen washed up.

Brian stood on the chair by the sink, pretending to be useful but really making a lot of mess on the floor. Helen put her arm round him and pressed her cheek against his.

'Now,' she said, 'you can help me make the sandwiches.'

'Want a rorange juice,' he demanded.

She was in the middle of pasting strawberry jam on some bread when she heard her parents walking through the little room where Brian slept. As soon as her mother opened the kitchen door, Helen looked anxiously up at her, and then immediately felt relieved. The grey shadows under her eyes had at last begun to disappear and she actually had some colour in her cheeks. She was wearing her pink cotton dressing gown, her long black hair scooped back untidily from her face.

'You're looking very peaky, Helen,' she said. 'You didn't have another bad dream, did you?'

'Too much reading,' her father said quickly.

'Yeah,' said Helen. 'I got this smashing book. I couldn't put it down last night.'

Helen finished making the sandwiches and then began to collect towels and buckets. Brian trailed after her as she walked through his room, down the long narrow passage and up to the door of the front room. She pushed it open. Her duffle-bag was hanging from the back of a chair over by the table.

'Want a rorange juice,' Brian said impatiently.

'In a minute.'

Brian scowled and sat down in the corridor, tracing the patterns on the faded lino with his fingers.

Helen picked up a towel and swimsuit and shoved them into the bag. She slung it over her shoulder and then leaned out of the window. The sea was only five minutes walk away.

Suddenly she felt a cold tingling sensation moving slowly down the back of her neck, right to the base of her spine. She whirled round but again she could see nothing. It was almost as if whatever it was slipped behind her back every time she moved. She pressed herself against the wall. Without thinking, her hand automatically went up to her throat as if to protect it. She pushed herself away.

'Come on, Brian,' she said.

She wanted to run, but instead she forced herself to

move casually, so as not to alarm him.

It wasn't until later that evening, in a pub down by the harbour, that Helen raised the subject of the room. The pub had a section for families, where they could sit and look out at all the boats coming in to moor. As soon as her mother had nipped off to the loo, Helen grabbed her chance.

'Dad,' she said quickly, 'could we change where my bed is and put it by the opposite wall?'

'Now don't you start on about that room again,' he warned.

'I just want the bed moved, that's all. I think it's the rattling of the windows that's scaring me.'

He smiled. 'Piece of cake, kiddo. We'll shift it as soon as we get back.'

Helen could have wept with relief. At least she'd feel a bit safer up by the wall of her parents' bedroom *and* she'd be nearer the light switch.

As soon as they returned, she and her father moved the bed. Her mother was all for it, too. 'I thought she was catching a bit of a chill by that window,' she remarked. Helen's father winked at her.

After Brian had gone to bed, Helen and her parents

played *Monopoly*. She didn't care for the game much. It was too slow. Montony, she called it. But it was different that night. Her mother was smiling. So was her dad. When it was time to go to bed, the last sound Helen heard before falling asleep was her parents chatting over a game of cards.

*

At first she thought it was the sound of her own breathing that had woken her, but she realised only too quickly that the breathing was coming from someone else. It was a rasping, asthmatic sort of breath. She sat up slowly and peered into the darkness.

A floorboard creaked. It came from the direction of the window. It was followed immediately by another creak. There was no mistaking it: someone was in the room. She listened, terrified, as the creaking grew louder and nearer, and the breathing turned into loud heaving gasps.

Helen jumped out of bed, turned on the light and hastily looked round the room. There was no one there. Still frightened, she backed out of the door. She would spend the rest of the night in the kitchen.

The dawn was a long time coming. Even when it was

light, Helen had no idea of the time. She pressed her ear up against the transistor radio, keeping the volume low. Anything to hear the comforting sound of a voice. At eight o'clock, she turned the sound up and began to lay the table. She was just pouring the milk into a jug, when the door knob moved. She jumped. Brian opened the door, his eyes sticky with sleep.

'Oh, Brian,' Helen said, picking him up and giving him a squeeze. 'I'm so glad to see you.'

'Want a rorange juice,' he said, rubbing his eyes.

As she sat him down, her parents walked in, still in their nightclothes.

'Hello, Dad,' she said brightly. 'Thought I'd give you a surprise breakfast. I'll put the kettle on.'

Her father eyed her suspiciously. 'I didn't hear you get up.'

'You ought to go back to bed,' said her mother. 'You look awful.'

'I'm all right.'

'Course she is,' said her father abruptly. 'Come on, let's get breakfast started.'

Helen knew that she had to get her father on his own but it wasn't until the afternoon that her chance came.

They were walking back to the flat after lunch in a café on the seafront. It was raining and her mother and Brian had rushed on ahead.

Helen grabbed her father by the arm. 'Dad, I've got to tell you about last night!'

'I know about last night,' he said. 'You had another of your nightmares, I suppose.'

They had stopped in a doorway to watch the wind whipping rain along the quay. People in summer clothes ran for shelter, holding newspapers over their heads.

'Please, Dad,' Helen said. 'I heard footsteps and this horrible breathing.'

He turned sharply to look at her. 'What?'

'Honest, Dad. It was over by the window. I thought it was a nightmare but I sat right up in bed and the sounds got louder and started to come towards me.'

Her father started to walk on. Helen had to run to keep up with him. 'But when I turned the light on,' she continued, 'there was no one there.'

'Well, there you are then,' he said. 'It must have been a bad dream.

Helen turned crossly away. 'You don't believe me, do

you?' She shoved her hands in the pockets of her jeans.

'Look, kiddo,' he began.

'Don't call me kiddo!'

'Well, you're acting like a kid!' he said angrily. 'These stupid nightmares!'

'They're *not* nightmares!' Helen yelled. 'I've told you I'm awake when it happens.' She strode briskly on ahead, swallowing her tears and rage. One minute adults expected you to be grown up, but if you tried to talk to them they refused to listen. If a grown-up had told him the story, he'd have listened all right.

Her father caught up with her and pulled her under his umbrella. He drew her close to him and gave her a hug. Before she could stop herself, Helen burst into tears. She was so tired. She'd give anything for a good night's sleep.

'Look,' her father said quietly, 'we've only got a few nights left.'

'I know, Dad, but I can't sleep in there again, I just can't.'

He took out a handkerchief and wiped her face. 'Don't worry, we'll sort something out.'

Later, in the kitchen, when Brian was asleep and her

mother had gone into the bedroom to put on some make-up, Helen's father took her to one side.

'Are you sure you'll be all right on your own?' he asked.

Helen nodded.

'We'll be at the pub down by the harbour. We'll only be gone an hour.'

'Don't worry, Dad. Stay longer if you want. I'll sit here in the kitchen.'

'We'll come straight back. You look like you could do with an early night.' He paused. 'I still don't know where we're going to put you.'

'I'll make up a bed in the bath,' she said, grinning.

He ruffled her hair. 'Attagirl.'

After her parents had left, Helen settled down at the kitchen table to read her book. It wasn't until later that she ventured into the front room. She had started to scribble down some verses for a song and had run out of paper. She knew that there was an exercise book on the table in her room.

'Oh, come on,' she whispered to herself. 'It's only a stupid room, and it isn't even dark yet.'

As soon as she entered the room, she sensed that the

evil that had been there had finally disappeared. It was as if it had been swept away by a mysterious force. She didn't feel scared any more. Relieved, she shut the door behind her, picked up the exercise book and sat down on the bed. She had thought of a word to rhyme with 'trail' and wanted to write it down immediately in case she forgot it. 'Hail,' she scribbled.

It was so cosy and comfortable in the room that she stayed there, writing busily. As she was racking her brain for a word to rhyme with 'saddle', her eyelids began to flicker. Gradually her head sank heavily onto the page and the pencil slipped from her fingers.

She had no idea what time it was when she woke. She only knew that it was dark. Light from the street outside spilled eerily across the carpet. She gripped the eiderdown, terrified, and struggled to shake off her fear but it was no good. She knew that something had woken her, and that it was still somewhere in the room. She turned her head slowly, taking in the tiled fireplace, the corner where an old gramophone stood near a handful of books on a shelf, past the window with its fluttering curtains, and along the wall to the table.

And then she saw him. A tall man standing in the

shadows. He had dark, straggly hair and a black beard. His arms hung by his sides, motionless.

Helen quickly turned her head away. It's a nightmare, she thought. I'm dreaming that I've woken up. She squeezed her eyes shut. Suddenly, there was a slight movement by the bed. She opened her eyes. The man was towering above her. I'm dreaming this, she thought. I'm dreaming, I'm dreaming, I'm dreaming. The figure leaned towards her. Please let me wake up soon. But the large shadow loomed nearer and she felt his hands grip her violently round the throat.

With one enormous effort she struggled free, and scrambled backwards, half-stumbling, half-falling over the back of the bed. Petrified she switched the light on. The room was empty.

She opened the door and padded swiftly and silently through Brian's room into the kitchen. Once there, she felt safe. She slid the window up and leaned out, gasping. She shivered and looked round for a sweater. It was then that she caught sight of her reflection in the small cracked mirror above the sink. She gave a startled cry, for there on her neck were the red marks made by the man's hands. She hadn't imagined him, after all.

She flung open the door into her brother's room, ran in, and dragged him out of bed.

*

Helen stood outside the pub by the harbour. Rain was lashing her face mercilessly, and her arms were aching from the effort of carrying Brian. He began to cry. She unzipped her sodden anorak and wrapped it round him. Then she found a door and slipped inside. A group of people were sitting on red plastic seats. A man behind the bar caught sight of her at once. ''Ere,' he said firmly. 'Outside!'

'I'm looking for me mum and dad,' said Helen. 'It's urgent.'

'Anyone own these two?' the man yelled.

Helen felt her face grow red as everyone turned to look at her.

'You'd best go home,' the man said.

Outside, the sea was hurling itself against the harbour wall. Helen could hardly see for the spray in her eyes. There was another pub in the distance. Still carrying Brian, she lowered her head and pushed against the swirl of wind.

After half an hour, she had run out of pubs.

Exhausted, she stumbled back along the beach and into a shelter where there were some wooden seats. Brian began to shiver. She was just rubbing his hands when she heard heavy footsteps approaching. She froze for an instant, and then she picked Brian up again, shot out of the shelter and ran. The footsteps quickened. Suddenly she was gripped from behind and twisted round. She peered up, terrified. It was a policeman.

He wouldn't listen to her either. All he said was something about getting dry and looking after the little chap and finding her parents. Even when they were both sitting in the warmth of the police station, with mugs of tea in their hands, the policeman just kept shaking his head and muttering, 'Kids!' It was only when Helen gave him her address that he began to look interested.

'It's in St Andrew's Road,' she said.

The sergeant, who had been standing with his back to them, swung round, startled. 'St Andrew's, did you say? A top floor flat?'

Helen nodded.

'And you say that you think a man was trying to kill you?'

'Yes, but when I turned on the light he wasn't there.'

'It wouldn't be number forty-three, would it?' the sergeant asked gently.

'Yes, that's right.'

'Woodfield,' he said to the young constable, 'see if a Mr and Mrs Robinson are in the top flat at number forty-three.'

'But they might not be there,' Helen blurted out. 'And if they aren't, I couldn't go back there on my own.'

'Don't worry, girl, you won't have to.'

Helen leaned back in relief, and sipped her tea. Brian was curled up on the bench beside her, half asleep.

Shortly after that, two policemen returned with her parents. Her mum was in a terrible state; her dad, furious.

'Where the hell have you been?' he yelled. 'Me and your mum have been worried sick.'

'Mr Robinson,' said the sergeant firmly. 'I'd like to speak to you and your wife in private.'

'We only left them for an hour –' her father began.

'Please,' said the sergeant.

Helen watched as they went into an adjoining room.

She did her best to eavesdrop from the bench but the two policemen in charge cottoned on, and started to talk loudly about some football match. When her parents reappeared, they looked stunned. Her father glanced across at her strangely.

'What's the matter, Dad?'

'Come on,' he said. 'We're going to move into a Bed-and-Breakfast.'

From then on, it was all a blur. All Helen could remember was a trip up a heavily carpeted staircase, and sitting in a warm bath, and being wrapped up in a towel by her father.

When she awoke the next morning, she found that she was lying in a small bed with a pink bedspread on it. Her mother was sitting at a dressing table, writing postcards.

'What time is it?' said Helen.

Her mother turned and smiled. 'Eleven o'clock. You've been asleep for twelve hours.' She came and sat on the bed and smoothed Helen's fringe gently behind her ears. 'Hurry up and get dressed. We'll go down to that fisherman's caff by the harbour and have a big fry-up.'

It wasn't until Helen had tucked into egg, bacon, fried bread, tomatoes, sausages and two large mugs of tea that her mother answered her questions about the flat.

'Are you sure you want to know?' she asked.

'Oh, Mum!' said Helen impatiently. 'Course I do.'

'Well,' began her mother, 'twenty-five years ago, a man murdered three children in that front room.'

'Blimey!' whispered Helen.

'And they were all girls.'

'They were strangled, weren't they?' said Helen quietly.

Her mother nodded.

Helen suddenly felt very cold. 'But is the man still alive, or what?'

'He was hanged.'

'But I felt his hands.' She looked hard at her mother. 'Honest, Mum, I really did.'

'Look, love, I believe you. I wish I'd known. I'd never have let you sleep in there.' She gave a shudder. 'Anyway, that's all over now. We'll have a lovely day together and stay at the Bed-and-Breakfast from now on.'

Helen gave a relieved sigh and gazed at the heavy drizzle which had begun to fall outside.

Suddenly she felt a hand on her shoulder. She gave a startled yell and whirled round. It was her father.

'Dad!' she cried. 'Don't do that! You scared me!'

'Sorry,' he said sheepishly. Both his hands were now firmly held behind his back.

'Dad!' Helen said suspiciously. 'What are you hiding?'

Slowly he revealed a large wooden object which he placed in her lap.

'A guitar!' she exclaimed.

It was a Spanish one. Just like a real folk singer's. She let her hands glide slowly over the wooden curves.

'I bought it at a second-hand shop round the corner,' her father said. 'I'm afraid it's a bit damp from the rain, though.' He took out a handkerchief and began to wipe it down.

'Oh, Dad,' Helen whispered, and beamed at him.

Within minutes, her head was bowed over the guitar and her thumb and fingers were plucking the strings. Gradually her parents' voices faded into the distance. She didn't even hear her brother asking for more orange juice, or the sound of the rain growing heavier. She had quite forgotten that she was sitting in a caff down by the harbour. And the murderous ghost? She had forgotten him, too.

Other authors in
the series

An interview with

J.K. Rowling

Creator of the bestselling
Harry Potter

J.K. Rowling is the author of the phenomenally successful Harry Potter series. She has won worldwide acclaim for all four of the books published so far in this seven-book series:
Harry Potter and the Philosopher's Stone,
Harry Potter and the Chamber of Secrets,
Harry Potter and the Prisoner of Azkaban and
Harry Potter and the Goblet of Fire.

An interview with

Anne Fine

The award-winning author
and children's Laureate

Anne Fine is a distinguished writer
for children of all ages, with over
40 books to her credit. She is the current
Children's Laureate, whose books include:
Bill's New Frock, Madame Doubtfire,
How To Write Really Badly, Goggle-Eyes,
Flour Babies and The Tulip Touch.

An interview with

Michael
Morpurgo

The award-winning author
of Kensuke's Kingdom

Michael Morpurgo is a best-selling,
award-winning author, adored by
children, teachers and parents alike.
He has written over 60 books, including:
Kensuke's Kingdom, The Sleeping Sword,
The Wreck of the Zanzibar, Why the Whales Came
and Arthur, High King of Britain.

An interview with

Jamila Gavin

The best-selling author of Coram Boy

Jamila Gavin had her first book
published in 1979 and has enjoyed
worldwide success ever since.
Her books include:
The Magic Orange Tree, Grandpa Chatterji,
The Surya Trilogy, Danger by Moonlight
and the award-winning Coram Boy.

An interview with

Jacqueline Wilson

The best-selling author
of The Illustrated Mum

Jacqueline Wilson has been a writer
since she was 17 and has had over
60 books published, including many
award-winners and best-sellers.
Her books include:
The Story of Tracy Beaker, Vicky Angel,
The Illustrated Mum, Sleep-overs,
Dustbin Baby and Secrets.

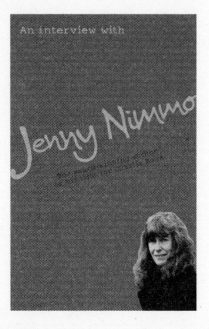

An interview with

Jenny Nimmo

The best-selling author of *Midnight for Charlie Bone*

Jenny Nimmo's enchanting children's
books have won awards, gained critical
acclaim and been widely adapted
for stage and screen.
Her magical new five-book series,
Children of the Red King, includes:
Midnight for Charlie Bone and
The Time Twister